MISSION CONTENTS

Profile - Action Man... 6

Overall Mission Brief... 8

MISSION BRIEF 1 10

On the Starting Block... 14

Attack of the X Robots.. 16

Quick on the Draw... 31

Poster.. 32

Profile Dr-X.. 34

MISSION BRIEF 2... 36

The Hunt is on.. 40

Rumble in the Jungle.. 42

Codename: Colour Attack... 56

Profile - Action Force.. 58

MISSION BRIEF 3... 60

All to Pieces... 64

X marks the Spot.. 66

Poster.. 80

Profile - No Face... 82

MISSION BRIEF 4... 84

Clocking Off.. 88

Dr. X Caught at Last.. 90

Battle on Island X.. 91

Mission Debriefing.. 106

Poster.. 108

ACTION MAN

ANNUAL 2005

Pedigree®

Published by Pedigree Books Limited
Beech Hill House, Walnut Gardens, Exeter, Devon EX4 4DH.
E-mail books@pedigreegroup.co.uk
Published 2004
Action Man and all related characters are trademarks of Hasbro
& are used with permission.
© 2004 Hasbro. Inc. All Rights Reserved.

Licensing by:

Hasbro

Properties
Group

£7.99

Although his past is shrouded in mystery, we do know that Action Man is 'the greatest hero of our time.' What you are about to read comes from his personnel file and is TOP SECRET.

SPECIAL SKILLS

Achieved 100% success rate in all of the following:
- Survival Skills
- Expert level driver/pilot of all known vehicles
- Champion adrenaline sportsman
- Unarmed combat
- Computers and Communication

ORIGINS

Name: Action Man
Place of Birth: Pawtucket, Rhode Island, USA.
Nationality: British:
Height: 1m 88cm
Weight: 93 kilogrammes
Born in the USA, Action Man grew up in the UK. His origins will be revealed in 2005.

ATTITUDES & ABILITIES

- Fearless courage and incredible dedication in fighting evil.
- Extremely fit and strong, with almost boundless energy.
- Speaks all known languages fluently.
- Highly intelligent. Can adapt to any situation.
- Great sense of humour, especially during times of great danger.

ACTION MAN
PROFILE

DISTINGUISHING FEATURES
- Scar on his right cheek.
- Tattoo on left arm.

Action Man has dedicated his life to battling the forces of evil. As the leader of Action Force, he is determined to bring Dr. X to justice, no matter how long it takes!

MISSION: ATTACK OF THE X ROBOTS

THE WORLD FACES ITS GREATEST THREAT, AS HUNDREDS OF DEADLY X ROBOTS MARCH ON ALL THE MAJOR CITIES.

THEIR MISSION - TOTAL AND UTTER DESTRUCTION! SURVEILLANCE SATELLITES AND TOP AGENTS HAVE DISCOVERED THAT THESE X ROBOTS ARE BEING CONTROLLED BY A MYSTERIOUS EVIL GENIUS, BENT ON CONTROLLING THE WORLD! CAN THIS BE DR. X? IMPOSSIBLE! HE MET HIS DOOM IN HIS LAST FEROCIOUS BATTLE AGAINST ACTION MAN. PERHAPS IT`S HIS HENCHMAN, NO FACE? WHOEVER IS BEHIND THIS THREAT TO HUMANITY HAS TO BE STOPPED! ONLY ONE PERSON HAS THE COURAGE, RESOURCES AND EXPERT FIGHTING SKILLS NECESSARY TO SAVE THE WORLD...

ACTION MAN

Will Action Man decide to call on the talents and abilities of Action Force, a crack team of agents specially trained by Action Man himself? Codename Red Wolf and Flynt, they are by far the best choice in dangerous situations. Fighting side by side with Action Man, Action Force are unstoppable!

There have been sightings of the hideously scarred No Face around the globe. Are these sightings true, or are our operatives being fed bad information to trick and confuse them? The truth must be uncovered. With his mastery of robotics, No Face could be the creator of these deadly X Robots!

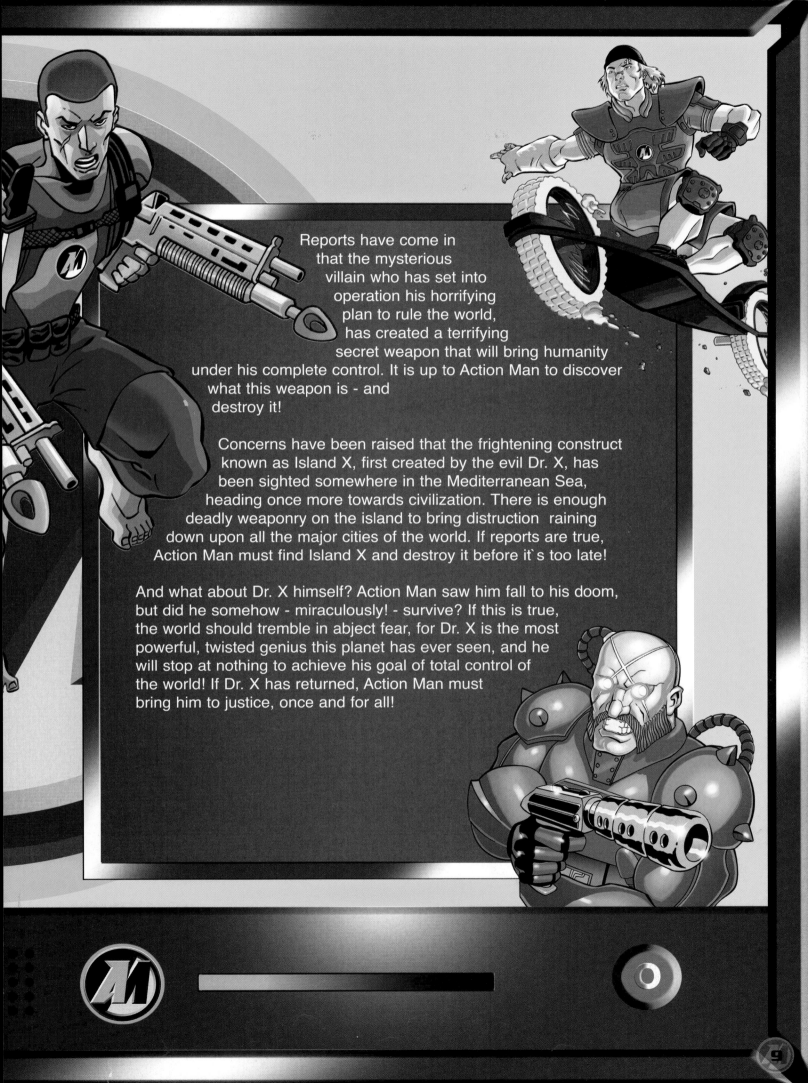

Reports have come in that the mysterious villain who has set into operation his horrifying plan to rule the world, has created a terrifying secret weapon that will bring humanity under his complete control. It is up to Action Man to discover what this weapon is - and destroy it!

Concerns have been raised that the frightening construct known as Island X, first created by the evil Dr. X, has been sighted somewhere in the Mediterranean Sea, heading once more towards civilization. There is enough deadly weaponry on the island to bring distruction raining down upon all the major cities of the world. If reports are true, Action Man must find Island X and destroy it before it`s too late!

And what about Dr. X himself? Action Man saw him fall to his doom, but did he somehow - miraculously! - survive? If this is true, the world should tremble in abject fear, for Dr. X is the most powerful, twisted genius this planet has ever seen, and he will stop at nothing to achieve his goal of total control of the world! If Dr. X has returned, Action Man must bring him to justice, once and for all!

TOP SECRET

MISSION BRIEF URGENT!

THE ANCIENT CITIES OF SAUDI ARABIA ARE BEING ATTACKED. REPORTS DETAIL THAT AN ARMY OF X ROBOTS ARE MARCHING ACROSS THE DESERT SANDS, OBLITERATING EVERYTHING IN THEIR PATH. THE PRECIOUS OIL FIELDS MUST BE PROTECTED AT ALL COST. HEAD DIRECTLY TO SUN-SCORCHED COUNTRY AND PREPARE FOR BATTLE!

SAUDI ARABIA

GEOGRAPHIC RECONNAISSANCE DATA

Location: Middle East. Largest country of Arabia, bordering the Persian Gulf and the Red Sea.
Capital: Riyadh
Range: 1,960,582 km.
Population: 22.7 million.
Temperature: June to August 50 C (122 F). Winter temperatures in northern and central regions can drop to below freezing.

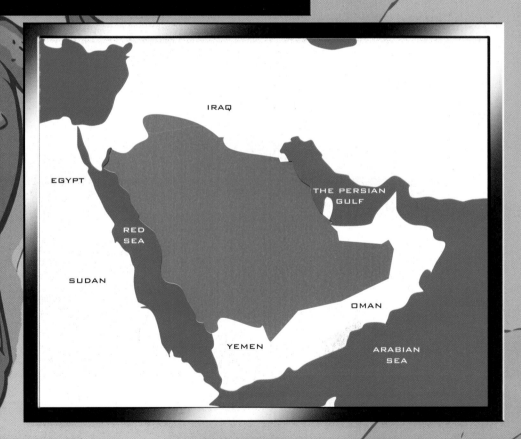

SURF ATTACK

- Polycarbonate and magnesium composite construction
- Light weight and very strong
- Water-jet engine
- High speed 360°
- 0 - 90 miles per hour - 8 seconds
- 2 x removable, front mounted laser guns
- 2 x multipurpose sidewinder missiles

AQUA BLASTER

- High powered water-jet rifle
- Jet strong enough to smash through concrete
- Touch sensitive keypad control
- Wide spray for multiple enemies, narrow pray for pin point accuracy
- Infa-red laser sight with targeting computer

ON THE STARTING BLOCK

12.AQU

9.MTRU

5.CER

10.AK

7.TEA

4.STER

2.ABLA

3.CKHQ

8.SUR

6.FAT

11.YRA

1.CIT

Special Agents, I need your help! That devious No Face has split the names of my latest equipment into blocks to confuse me. Can you place the blocks in the right order to spell the names properly? Write the numbers of the blocks in the answer grid provided.

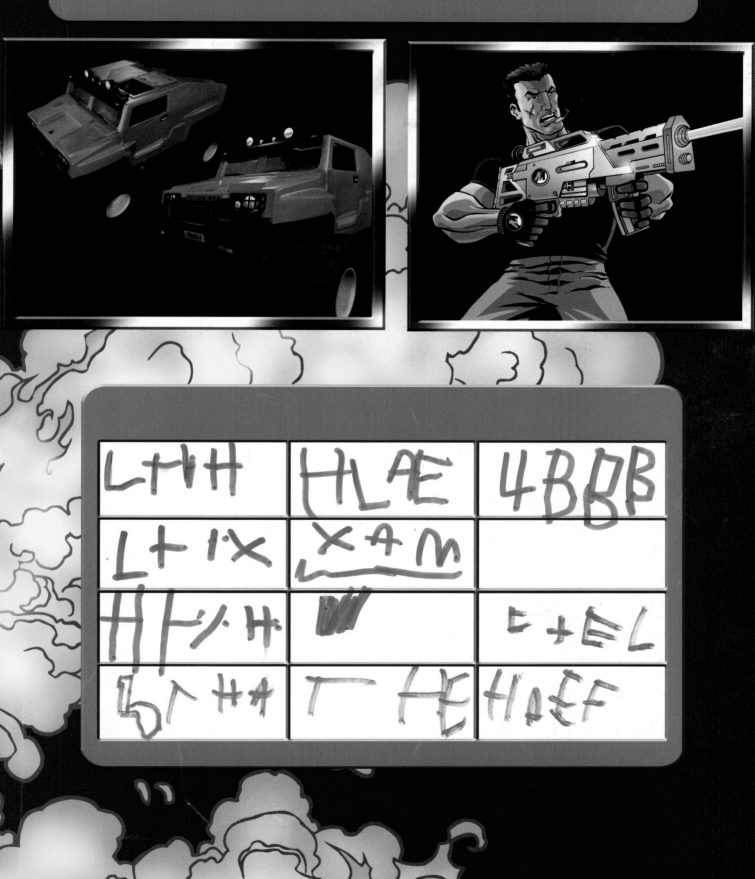

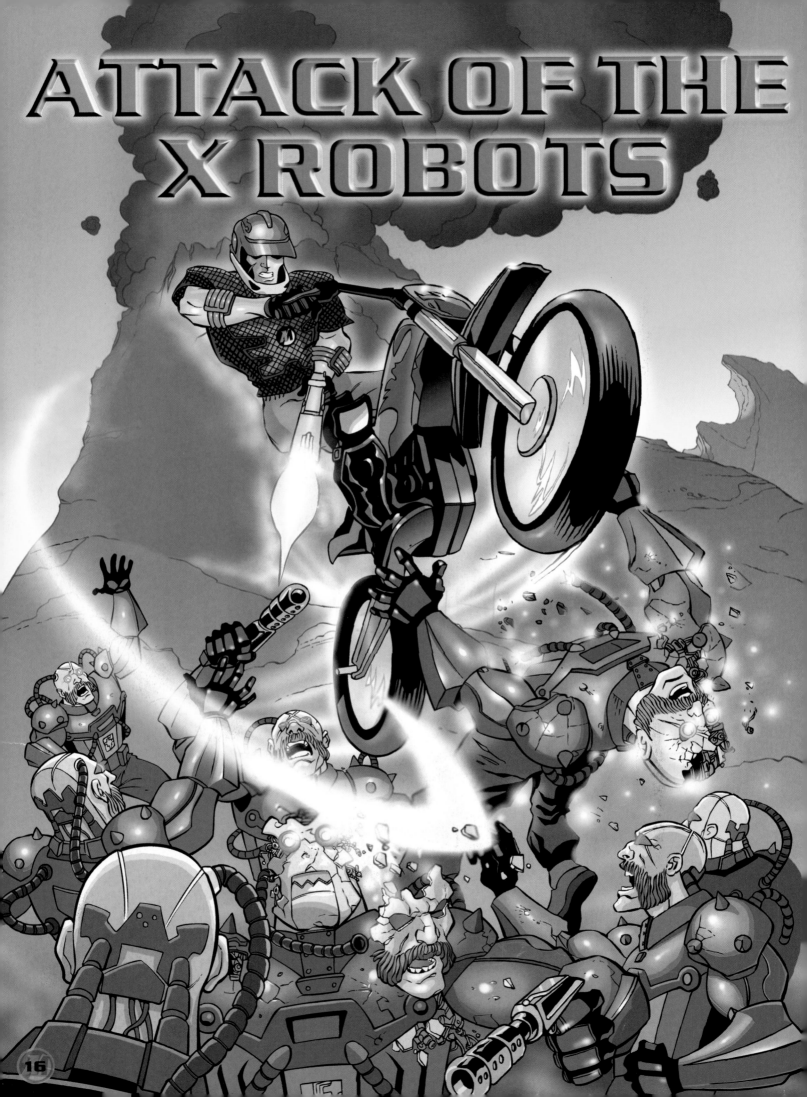

SPEED AND ACCURACY WIN THE DAY!

KAA-BOOOM!

DOWN - - AND OUT!

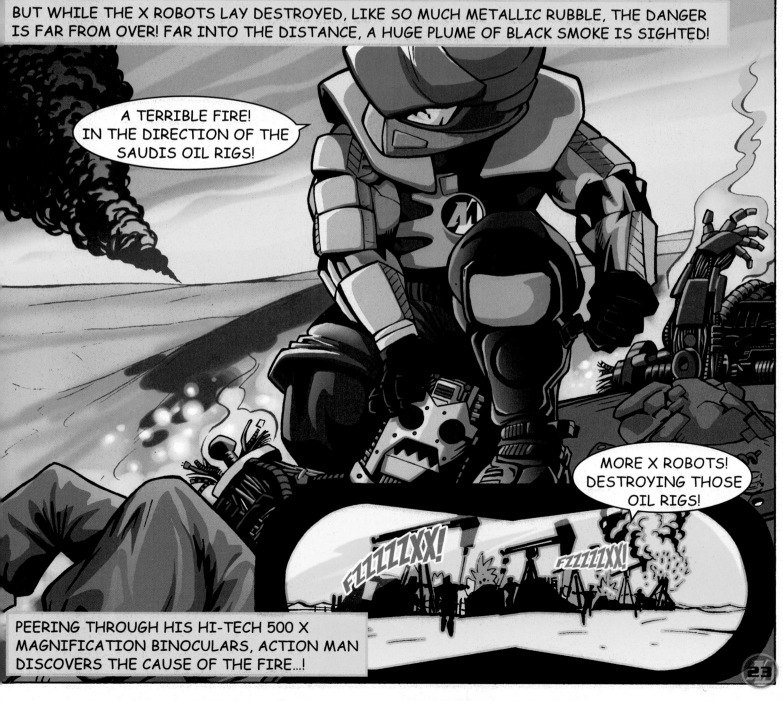

BUT WHILE THE X ROBOTS LAY DESTROYED, LIKE SO MUCH METALLIC RUBBLE, THE DANGER IS FAR FROM OVER! FAR INTO THE DISTANCE, A HUGE PLUME OF BLACK SMOKE IS SIGHTED!

A TERRIBLE FIRE! IN THE DIRECTION OF THE SAUDIS OIL RIGS!

MORE X ROBOTS! DESTROYING THOSE OIL RIGS!

FZZZZXX!

FZZZZXX!

PEERING THROUGH HIS HI-TECH 500 X MAGNIFICATION BINOCULARS, ACTION MAN DISCOVERS THE CAUSE OF THE FIRE...!

23

USING A REMOTE CONTROL WRISTWATCH DEVICE, ACTION MAN SENDS HIS WONDERFUL ULTRA MTX INTO BATTLE!

CLICK! CLICK!

WHOOOSSSH!

BOOMMFF!

WELL, THAT CUT HIM DOWN TO SIZE!

THREE MORE X ROBOTS APPEAR, WITH BUT ONE DESIRE IN THEIR ELECTRONIC BRAINS - DESTROY ACTION MAN!

THIS INFORMATION MEANS THAT THERE`S ONLY ONE THING FOR ACTION MAN TO DO!

I HAVE TO FIND THIS X ROBOT FACTORY AND DESTROY IT...

NEVER ONE TO BE EMBARRASSED IN ASKING FOR HELP, HE MAKES CONTACT WITH BRAVE ALLIES HE KNOWS HE CAN TRUST IN THE FACE OF SUCH EXTREME DANGER!

AND FOR THAT, I`M GOING TO NEED HELP!

29

THERE`S ONLY ONE TEAM THAT ACTION MAN CAN DEPEND ON! ONLY ONE TEAM WHO WILL BE WILLING TO FIGHT BY HIS SIDE, NO MATTER WHAT THE ODDS!
IT`S TIME TO CALL IN ...
ActionForce
AF

QUICK ON THE DRAW

Draw this picture of Action Man, square by square, into the blank grid and then colour it in!

No FACE IS AN OCCASIONAL HENCHMAN TO DR. X, BUT HE HAS HIS OWN HIDDEN AGENDA.

DISTINGUISHING FEATURES

A TERRIBLE ACCIDENT DURING A GETAWAY HAS LEFT NO FACE`S ENTIRE BODY HORRIBLY SCARRED.

SPECIAL SKILLS

- EXPERT IN ROBOTICS AND NANO TECHNOLOGY.
- ONE OF THE WORLD`S TOP SWORD FIGHTING AND FENCING CHAMPIONS.
- EXPERT MOTORCYCLE RIDER.

ATTITUDES & ABILITIES

- BLAMES THE WORLD FOR HIS DISFIGUREMENT.
- IS CRUEL, DEVIOUS AND CALCULATING.
- EXTREMELY DEADLY IN COMBAT.

NO FACE
PROFILE

ORIGINS

NAME: NO FACE (GERRARD DE VISAGE)

PLACE OF BIRTH: BRUSSELS, BELGIUM

HEIGHT: 1M 85CM

WEIGHT: 75 KILOGRAMMES

BORN INTO A WEALTHY BELGIUM FAMILY, NO FACE HAS BEEN DENIED HIS INHERITANCE AS HE CANNOT PROVE HIS IDENTITY.

NO FACE IS ALMOST AS DEADLY AND DANGEROUS AS DR. X AND MUST NOT BE APPROACHED. IF SIGHTED, CALL IN ACTION FORCE!

TOP SECRET

MISSION BRIEF URGENT!

Urgent! There have been multiple sightings of the mad genius No Face in the depths of the rainforests of Borneo. Action Force is on the way to meet with you. If reports are true and No Face is working at a secret factory, producing the deadly X Robots, both it and they must by destroyed. This threat to world peace must be contained at any cost!

GEOGRAPHIC RECONNAISSANCE DATA

BORNEO

Location: South East Asia.
Capital: Brunei. Range: 738,150 sq km.
Population: 12.5 million. Temperature: 23-33 C all year round, cooler in mountain regions.
Notable facts: *Third largest island in the world.

*Most of the population of Borneo live along rivers.

ULTRA MTX

- Carbon fibre and magnesium composite construction
- Adjustable ceramic shock absorbers
- 24 speed automatic gearbox
- Puncture proof tyres
- 2000cc engine plus boosters
- 0-70 miles per hour - 9 Seconds
- 95 miles per hour top speed
- 2 x sidewinder missiles

Armoured helmet
- Kevlar construction with anti-glare visor
- Built in GPS*

*Global Positioning System - allows action man to see where he is any where in the world and to download information from any of the satellites orbiting the earth. Also used to track enemy locations and movements

AIR ATAK

- Carbon fibre and aluminium construction
- Turbo boosted rotor blades
- 0 - 90 miles per hour - 7 seconds
- Highly maneuverable
- Voice activated controls
- Computer controlled flight
- Built in GPS (Global Positioning System)
- Laser rifle - 100 pulses per minute
- 2 x sidewinder missiles

HELMET

- Microphone for voice commands
- Laser-powered goggles
- Infa-red, night vision
- Anti-glare visor

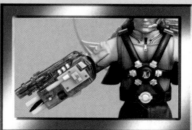

Action Man is on the hunt for Dr. X before he puts into operation his latest deadly plan to rule the world! Can you help him choose the right entrance through the maze to reach his Number One enemy? But watch out - X Robots are waiting to destroy you!

Answer: The correct entrance is B!

41

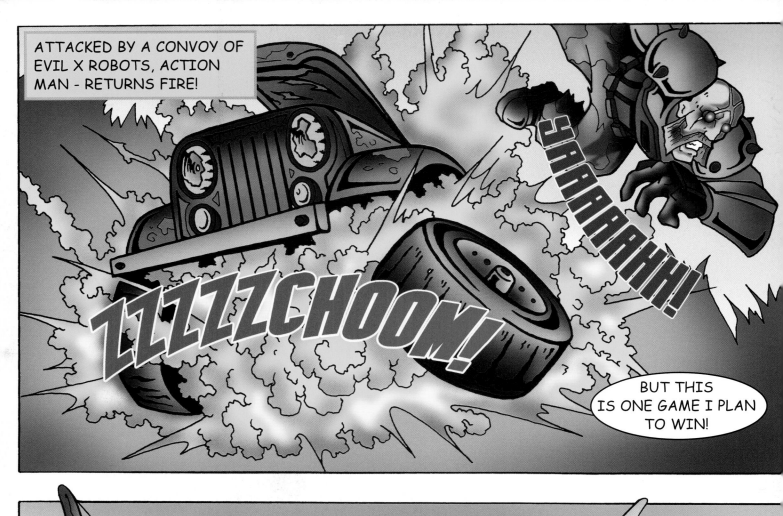

ATTACKED BY A CONVOY OF EVIL X ROBOTS, ACTION MAN - RETURNS FIRE!

YAAAAAHH!

ZZZZZZCHOOM!

BUT THIS IS ONE GAME I PLAN TO WIN!

COME TO BORNEO AND HAVE SOME FUN, ACTION MAN TOLD US, FLYNT!

HEY, RED WOLF! FOR US - THIS IS FUN!

CHUCKLE!

LAYING IN WAIT ARE HIS BRAVE OPERATIVES, RED WOLF AND FLYNT, OTHERWISE KNOWN AS.....

ActionForce 7

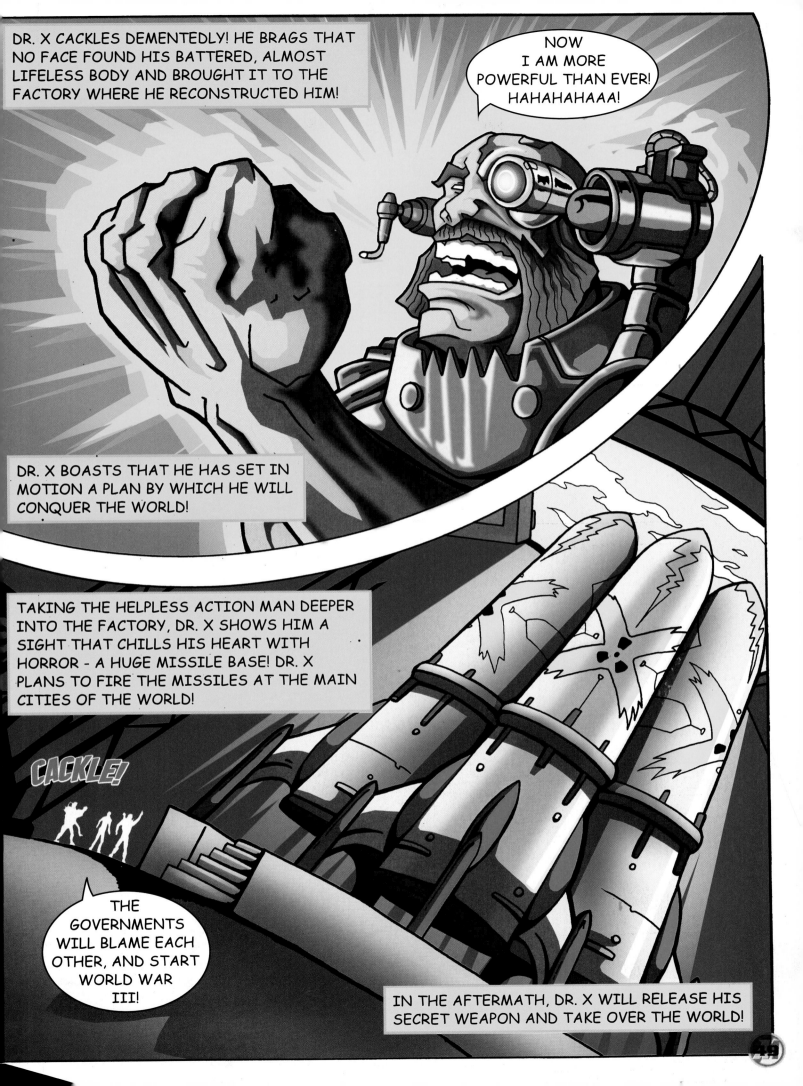

Oh, no! The evil Dr. X`s latest plan to take control of the world is to suck the colour out of all living things! Can you help Action Man save the day - once again! - by colouring in this action-packed picture?

FLYNT PROFILE

ORIGINS

NAME: FLYNT

PLACE OF BIRTH: SURFER'S PARADISE, AUSTRALIA.

HEIGHT: 1M 83CM

WEIGHT: 79 KILOGRAMMES

WHEN HE WAS 19, FLYNT WAS CROWNED WORLD SURF CHAMPION.

SPECIAL SKILLS

- EXPERT IN ALL ADRENALINE SPORTS
  (INCLUDING SURFING, DIRT SURFING, BASE JUMPING AND ROCK CLIMBING)
- EXPERT WITH A BOOMERANG.
- ONE OF THE TOP COMPUTER PROGRAMMERS IN THE WORLD.

ATTITUDES & ABILITIES

- LOVES BIG WAVES AND FAST CARS.
- BRASH AND LOUD, FLYNT ENJOYS LIFE TO THE FULL.
- WORLD SURF CHAMPION.

ACTION FORCE

With Action Man as their leader, Red Wolf and Flynt make up the two other members of Action Force, a special attack unit who's main goal is to track down and capture the deadly Dr.X!

RED WOLF PROFILE

ORIGINS

Name: Red Wolf
Place of Birth: Grand Rapids, USA.
Height: 1m 88cm
Weight: 88 kilogrammes
At 15, he spent a month tracking down a deadly grizzly bear.
In honour of his heroism he was given the name Red Wolf.

SPECIAL SKILLS

- Expert tracker and hunter, and in unarmed combat.
- Expert in survival and natural remedies.
- Eagle-eyed bowman.

ATTITUDES & ABILITIES

- Intuitive and spiritual master of the outdoors.
- A man of few words but a wry sense of humour.
- Can communicate with animals.

 # TOP SECRET

MISSION BRIEF
URGENT!

RECEIVING URGENT MESSAGE FROM THE FRENCH PRESIDENT - X ROBOTS ATTACKING THE EIFFEL TOWER. URGENT SUPPORT REQUIRED. THIS MAY BE A PLOY TO DELAY CAPTURE OF DR. X. MAKE COMMAND DECISION AS TO THE SUCCESS OF BATTLING X ROBOTS - FULL USE OF ACTION FORCE RECOMMENDED. BUT CAPTURE OF DR. X IS URGENT BEFORE HE HAS A CHANCE TO USE HIS DEADLY SECRET WEAPON AGAINST THE WORLD. HE MUST BE STOPPED!

FRANCE

GEOGRAPHIC RECONNAISSANCE DATA

Location: Western Europe, bordering the Bay of Biscay and English Channel between Belgium and Spain, and bordering the Mediterranean Sea between Italy and Spain.
Capital: Paris
Range: Total Area 547,030 sq km.
Land Area: 545,630 sq km.
Population: 59,494,800
Temperature: Cool/freezing winters and mild summers, but mild winters and hot summers along the Mediterranean Sea.
Notable Facts: *Largest Western European nation.

*The Eiffel Tower and Arc de Triomphe are world famous monuments.

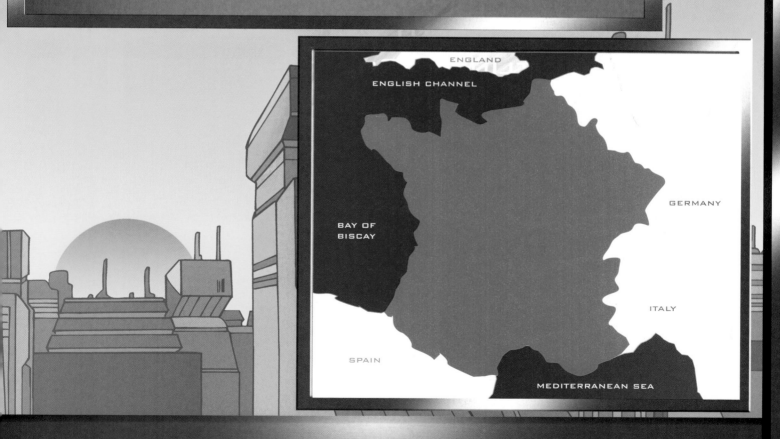

CITY RACER

- Carbon fibre and titanium sub-frame
- Kevlar armoured bodywork
- All weather, multi surface racing tyres (fluid filled to prevent punctures)
- Front mounted triple turbo engine
- four - wheel drive
- 0 - 140 miles per hour - 10 seconds
- Stealth control computer with GPS (global positioning system)
- 2 x spoiler mounted sidewinder missiles
- 2 x retractable laser canons
- Removable "Ninja" blade style hub caps

KONGO

- Captured by hunters in the jungles of africa for the evil no face
- Rescued from his cruel fate by action man
- Always ready to fight at action mans side at a moments notice
- Fearless and naturally powerful
- Armed with a rocket launcher back-pack
- Capable of taking on whole armies single handed

ALL TO PIECES!

Can you fit the correct missing pieces of this action-packed picture into the empty spaces to complete the jigsaw?

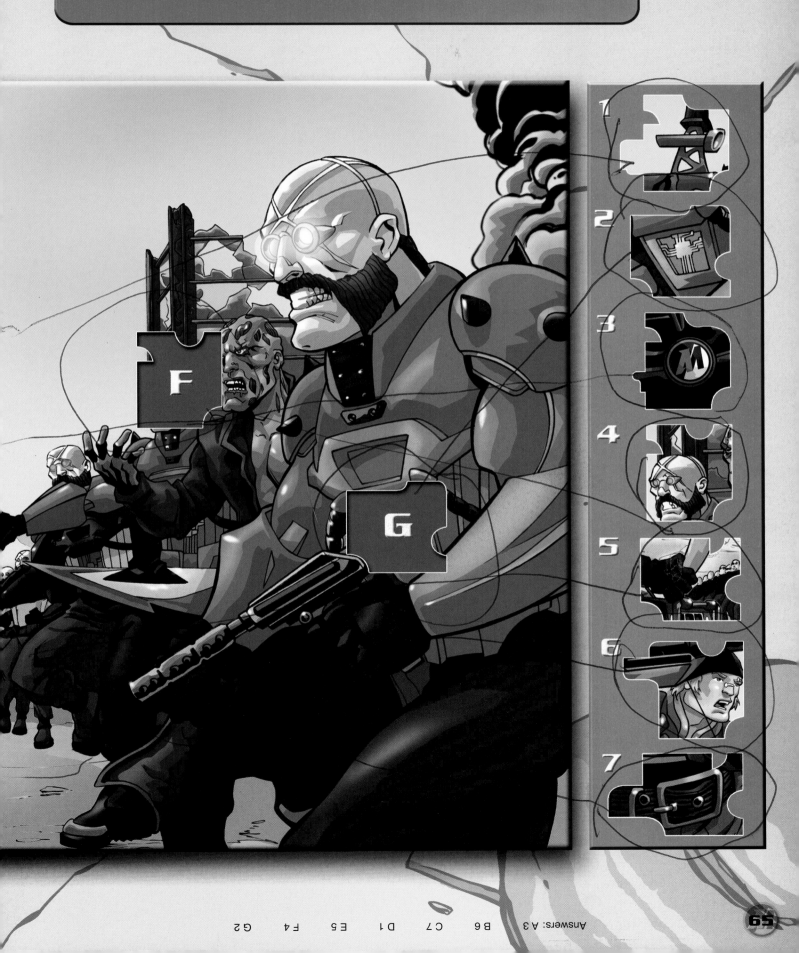

Answers: A3 <inverse>B6</inverse> <inverse>C7</inverse> <inverse>D1</inverse> <inverse>E5</inverse> <inverse>F4</inverse> <inverse>G2</inverse>

FOLLOWING DR. X AND NO FACE TO FRANCE, HE COUNTERATTACKS IN HIS SUPREMELY FAST AND ALL-POWERFUL - CITY RACER!

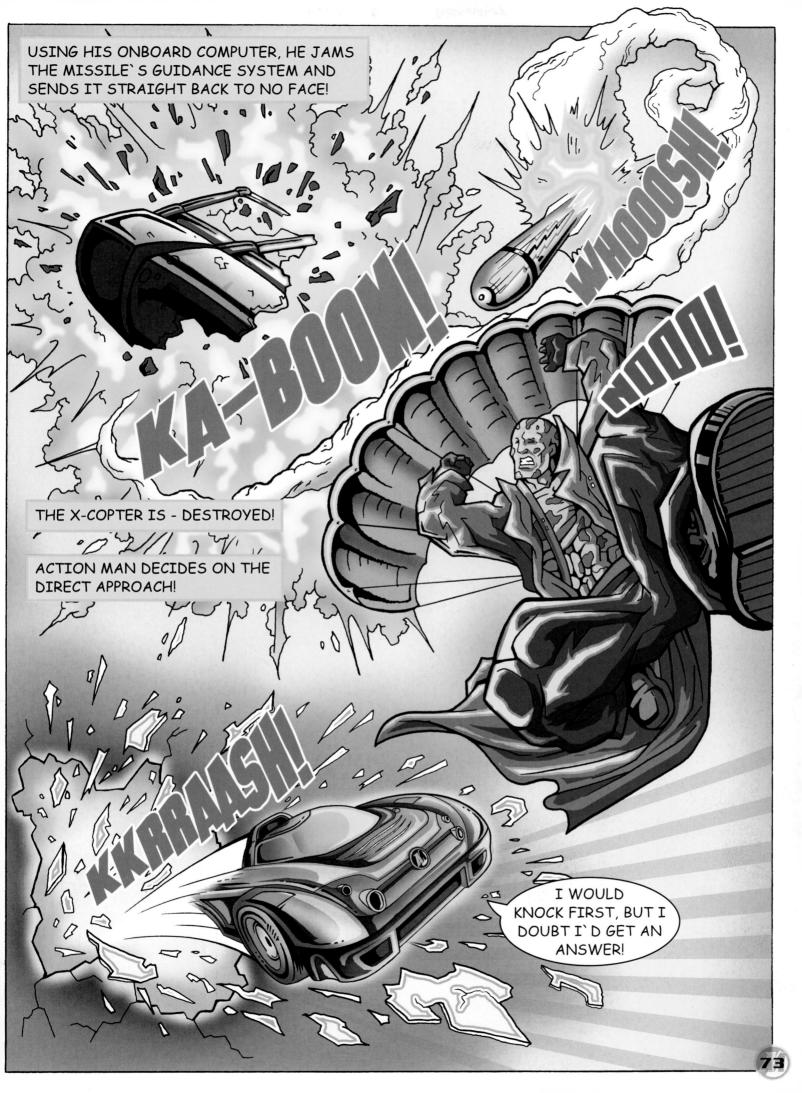

ACTION MAN`S CITY RACER FALLS TOWARDS CERTAIN DOOM!

LOOKS LIKE I`M IN FOR A BUMPY LANDING!

QUICKLY FLICKING A SWITCH INSIDE THE VEHICLE, HE BREATHES A SIGH OF RELIEF AS THE CITY RACER`S FAIL SAFE MECHANISM RELEASES A LARGE PARACHUTE TO SET HIM GENTLY TO THE GROUND.

THEN AGAIN, MAYBE NOT!

I`VE DISCOVERED WHERE DR. X AND NO FACE HAVE ESCAPED TO...!

ACTION FORCE, HAVING DESTROYED THE REST OF THE X ROBOTS, SHOWER DOWN CONGRATULATIONS ON A JOB WELL DONE - BUT ACTION MAN HAS NO TIME FOR WELL MEANING ACCOLADES!

THE DREADED... ISLAND X!

DR. X IS A DIABOLICAL MEGALOMANIAC WHO'S ONE AIM IN LIFE IS TO RULE THE WORLD. ONLY THE COURAGE OF ACTION MAN AND HIS ACTION FORCE TEAM CAN STOP HIM. RESCUED FROM CERTAIN DOOM BY NO-FACE, HE IS NOW EVEN MORE CRUEL AND DEADLY THAN EVER BEFORE...

ATTITUDES & ABILITIES

- CRUEL, COWARDLY AND CUNNING.
- AN INSECURE, TWISTED GENIUS, STRUGGLING FOR CONTROL AND POWER AT ANY PRICE.
- EXTREMELY FIT AND STRONG.
- CHESS GRANDMASTER.
- SPEAKS 20 LANGUAGES.

DISTINGUISHING FEATURES

- X TATTOO ON CHEST.
- WHIPLASH HAIR STRENGTHENED WITH TRILITHIUM WHICH CAN CUT THROUGH CONCRETE!
- EXTREMELY POWERFUL BIONIC ARM.
- X- RAY EYE THAT ALLOWS THE DOCTOR TO SEE THROUGH ANYTHING.

DR. X
PROFILE

SPECIAL SKILLS

- TECHNOLOGY, BIO-CHEMISTRY AND GENETICS EXPERT.
- UNARMED COMBAT MASTER.
- EXPERT SURVIVAL SKILLS.
- HIDDEN CHEST CAVITY HOUSES TWO HIGH-POWERED ROCKET LAUNCHERS THAT CAN BE FIRED IN LESS THAN A SECOND!

ORIGINS

NAME: DR. X
(COUNT LASZLO HUSZAR II)
PLACE OF BIRTH: BUDAPEST, HUNGARY
HEIGHT: 1M 930CM
WEIGHT: 102 KILOGRAMMES
DR X. IS THE WORLD'S GREATEST CRIMINAL AND FEARED UNDERWORLD LEGEND. HE IS ACTION MAN'S ARCH ENEMY.

DR. X IS THE GREATEST THREAT TO WORLD PEACE TODAY! ONLY ACTION MAN AND THE ACTION FORCE TEAM HAVE THE POWER AND ABILITIES TO STOP HIM!

TOP SECRET

MISSION BRIEF URGENT!

THE WORLD IS ON THE EDGE OF DISASTER. IT IS URGENT THAT DR. X`S DEADLY MIND CONTROL GAS IS LOCATED AND DESTROYED. ISLAND X HAS BEEN LOCATED DRIFTING IN THE MEDITERRANEAN SEA, CLOSE TO THE BALEARIC ISLANDS OF MAJORCA, MINORCA AND IBIZA. USE WHATEVER FORCE NECESSARY TO STOP THIS MADMAN BEFORE HE CAN SET IN MOTION HIS GRAND DREAMS OF RULING THE WORLD. THE FATE OF MANKIND IS IN YOUR HANDS. GOOD LUCK!

GEOGRAPHIC RECONNAISSANCE DATA

ISLAND X

Location: Mediterranean Sea

Range: 520 x 520 sq km

Temperature: Sub-zero in the Ice Zone to the north, 50C (122F) in the south.

Population: 1 (Dr. X) Sometimes populated with henchmen.

Notable Facts: *Island X is a man-made, mechanical island devised and built by the mad genius, Dr. X. The island is filled with deadly death traps and the most powerful weapons ever created.

*There are four different zones on the island: Ocean Zone filled with bloodthirsty, genetically-engineered sharks; the aforementioned Ice Zone where no man can survive for long in such extreme temperatures; Extreme Mountain with specially bred, vicious polar bears; Jungle Zone guarded by fierce Aztec warriors.

MISSION TECH

- Multi purpose battle suit is one of action mans most amazing weapons in his fight against evil
- Light weight Kevlar body armour and helmet protects against most forms of attack
- Back Pack contains - Digital radio
  High power binoculars
  Digital zoom camera
  Wap phone
  Explosives
  Miniature rockets
  Missile packs
- Built in jet-pack for air assaults
- 2 x high powered rifles with laser sights
- Kevlar helmet with built in GPS computer

TEAM TRUCK HQ

- EQUALLY USEFUL AS A SURVEILLANCE OR ATTACK VEHICLE
- STEALTH TECHNOLOGY CREATES IMAGES OF TEAM TRUCK H.Q. IN OTHER LOCATIONS TO CONFUSE ENEMY
- ON BOARD COMPUTER CAN CONNECT TO ANY OTHER COMPUTER IN THE WORLD AND TO ORBITING SATELLITES IN SPACE
- 10,000 CC, V12 ENGINE GIVES INCREDIBLE POWER
- 0 - 180 MILES PER HOUR - 7 SECONDS
- LIGHT WEIGHT TITANIUM FRAME WITH KEVLAR ARMOUR
- EXTENDABLE HYDROFOIL WINGS FOR TRAVEL ACROSS WATER
- PUNCTURE-PROOF ALL-TERRAIN TYRES FOR TRAVEL ON ANY SURFACE
- 2 x SIDEWINDER MISSILES, 4 x LASER CANONS

CLOCKING OFF

By telling the times listed below, you will discover words that have something to do with the world`s greatest secret agent - Action Man!

A - FIVE MINUTES PAST NINE.
B - HALF PAST THREE.
C - TEN TO EIGHT.
D - TWENTY PAST TWO.
E - SEVEN O`CLOCK.
F - TWENTY FIVE PAST ELEVEN.

11 ACE
10 TACK
9 AMTX
8 OTS
OLF
7

12

1

2

3

4

5

6

AND

ULTA

NOF

XROB

XISL

REDW

SURFA

CAUGHT AT LAST

Who has finally caught Dr. X? Follow the lengths of rope to find out!

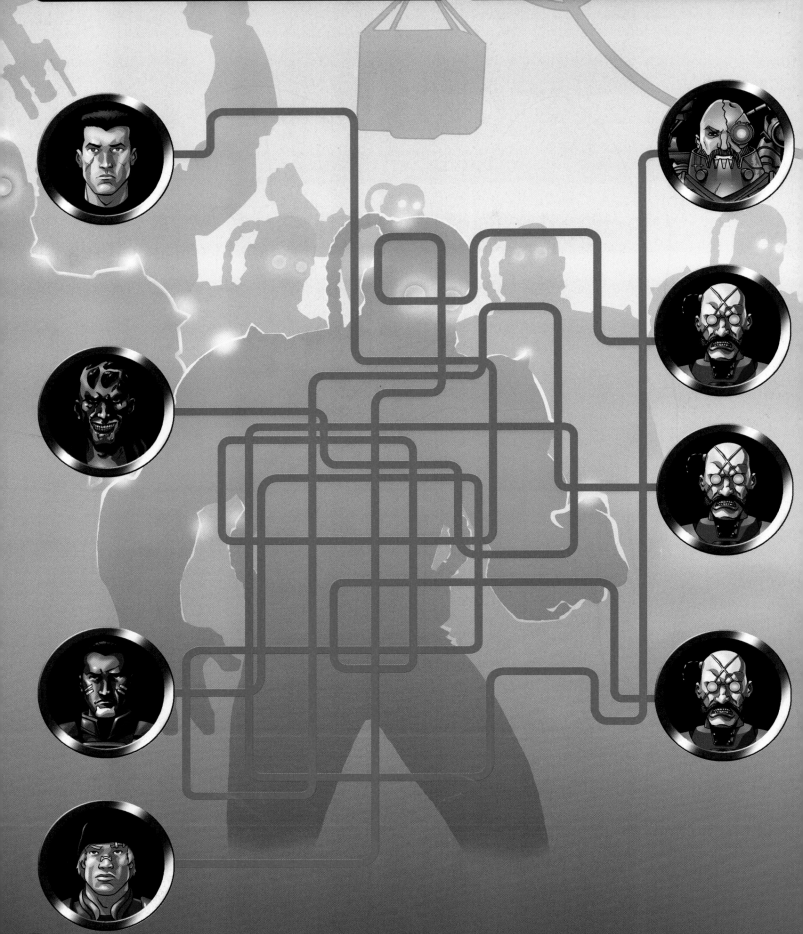

Answer: No Face has caught Dr. X! (Boy, is he going to be in trouble!)

TEAM TRUCK H.Q. - THE MOST SOPHISTICATED, STATE OF THE ART BATTLE VEHICLE EVER DESIGNED!

VRROOOM!

USING TEAM TRUCK H.Q.'S HIGHLY SENSITIVE GLOBAL POSITIONING SYSTEM (GPS), BOUNCING SIGNALS OFF SURVEILLANCE SATELLITES CIRCLING THE PLANET, ACTION MAN SOON LOCATES DR. X'S HIDDEN BASE - INSIDE A DORMANT VOLCANO!

VRROOOM!

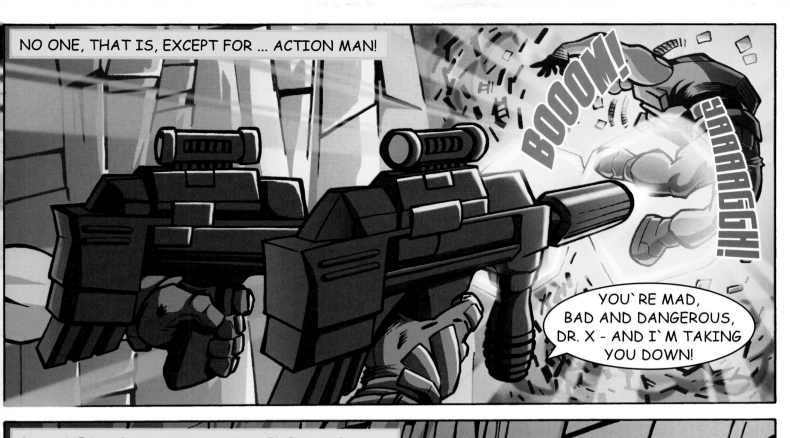

NO ONE, THAT IS, EXCEPT FOR ... ACTION MAN!

BUT THE DIABOLICAL DR. X IS DETERMINED THAT THIS TIME, HE WILL STAND TRIUMPHANT! HIS CHEST CAVITY SLIDES OPEN, RELEASING TWO DEADLY MINIATURE MISSILES - STRAIGHT TOWARDS ACTION MAN!

101

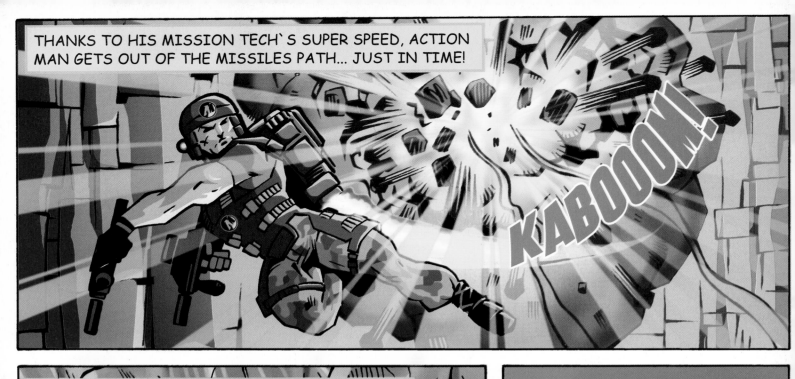

THANKS TO HIS MISSION TECH'S SUPER SPEED, ACTION MAN GETS OUT OF THE MISSILES PATH... JUST IN TIME!

KABOOOM!

UNFORTUNATELY FOR THE DEMENTED DR. X, HE PAYS THE PENALTY FOR HIS MADNESS! THE WALL OF THE VOLCANO CRASHES DOWN UPON HIM!

ACTION MAN HAS NO TIME TO WASTE! THE FATE OF HUMANITY RESTS IN HIS HANDS!

AAAGGGHH!

THOSE MISSILES MUST BE STOPPED!

WHOOSH!

AS SHUDDERING VIOLENT SHOCKWAVES AND EARTHQUAKES TEAR APART ISLAND X, ACTION MAN, RED WOLF AND FLYNT ESCAPE IN THE NICK OF TIME IN THEIR TEAM TRUCK H.Q.!

WELL, I`VE ONLY GOT ONE THING TO SAY - -

VVRROOMMSSH!

YET AGAIN THE WORLD HAS BEEN SAVED BY THE COURAGE AND BRAVERY OF ACTION FORCE, AND THE GREATEST HERO OF ALL TIME...

ACTION MAN

- - DR. X`S MAD PLANS HAVE BEEN WELL AND TRULY - SUNK!

CHUCKLE!

MISSION DEBRIEFING

REQUESTING MISSION ASSISTANCE!

WITH DR. X DEFEATED, ACTION MAN MUST BE DEBRIEFED ON HIS MOST DANGEROUS MISSION YET BEFORE HE CAN TAKE A WELL EARNED BREAK.

HE IS PUTTING HIS TRUST IN YOU TO ANSWER ALL NECESSARY QUESTIONS ABOUT THE MISSION. YOU HAVEN'T LET HIM DOWN YET! FINALLY, A PERSONAL WORD OF THANKS TO YOU FROM ACTION MAN HIMSELF: "THANK YOU FOR YOUR MISSION ASSISTS, SPECIAL AGENTS. I COULDN'T HAVE DONE IT WITHOUT YOU. KEEP UP THE GREAT WORK!"

MISSION ONE: SANDS OF DOOM

Q1: Which country first fell victim to attack by the deadly X Robots?
A) Yugoslavia?   B) Grimshore-By-the-Sea   C) Saudi Arabia

Q2: What vehicle was used by Action Man to stop the X Robots from attacking the city?
A) Surf Atack   B) Surf Aaachoo   C) Aqua Atack

Q3: The X Robots tried to destroy something in the desert that would have plunged the world into chaos. Was it:
A) Oil Wells   B) Television transmission signals   C) Tea bags

Q4: How did Action Man download information from the defeated X Robot's memory banks. Did he use:
A) A laptop   B) A mobile phone   c) His old granny

MISSION TWO - RUMBLE IN THE JUNGLE

Q5: Which courageous fighting team did Action Man call upon to help him break into No Face`s hidden factory?
A) Action Stations   B) Laurel and Hardy   C) Action Force

Q6: Red Wolf is the codename of one of the Action Force team. What is the name of the other agent?
A) Flint   B) Flynt   C) Marble

Q7: What was No Face creating at the secret factory in the jungles of Borneo?
A) X Robots   B) A new flavour of ice cream   C) Mind Control Gas

Q8: Action Man was captured in the bone-crunching grip of an X Robot. Who saved him?
A) King Kong   B) Red Wolf   C) Kongo

MISSION THREE: X MARKS THE SPOT!

Q9: The X Robots attacked a famous monument in Paris, France. Was it:
A) The Arc de Triomphe   B) Pierre`s Snail & Onion Stall   C) The Eiffel Tower

Q10: In which X-shaped building was Dr. X creating his deadly mind control gas?
A) X Bank   B) X Tower   C) X Pyramid

Q11: Action Man thought he had captured Dr. X inside the X building. But Dr X turned out to be…
A) A cardboard cutout   B) A mannequin   C) A hologram

Q12: Dr. X left a deadly present for Action Man inside the X building. Was it:
A) A yo-yo   B) A time bomb   C) A pogo stick

MISSION FOUR: DEADLY BATTLE ON ISLAND X!

Q13: Action Man and Action Force landed on Island X at which Zone?
A) Ocean Zone   B) Jungle Zone   C) No Parking Zone

Q14: Where was Dr. X`s secret base?
A) Inside a cave   B) Inside a temple   C) Inside a dormant volcano

Q15: Action Man and No Face had a deadly duel on motorbikes. What weapons did they use?
A) Medieval Lances   B) Pillows   C) Swords

Q16: Dr. X met his doom when Action Man sent the evil genius`s own weapon back down into the volcano. Was it:
A) A missile   B) An X-Copter   C) A cuddly toy

Answers
1: c) Saudi Arabia, 2: a) Surf Atack, 3: a) Oil Wells, 4: b) A mobile phone,
5: c) Action Force, 6: b) Flynt, 7: a) X Robots, 8: c) Kongo,
9: c) The Eiffel Tower, 10: b) X Tower, 11: c) A hologram,
12: b) A time bomb, 13: a) Ocean Zone, 14: c) A dormant volcano,
15: c) Swords, 16: A missile.

http://www.actionman.com

107

THE END...